# India

Components

<u>Folktale:</u> The unit begins with a folktale that serves as a springboard for the cross-curricular activities. The story can be read at several points in the unit -- to introduce the unit, before or after the Pocket Chart Activity, and in conjunction with the Story Mat.

<u>Folktale Follow-Up:</u> Questions in the Folktale Follow-Up enable children to discover some of the unique aspects and customs of the culture. Through the story and the illustrations, children become aware of such topics as dress, food, language, and housing.

<u>Pocket Chart Strips and Activities:</u> A portion of the story that lends itself to chanting has been rendered on pocket chart strips. Whole language suggestions are included. Children can learn the chant before or after reading the story; once they know the chant, they can join in wholeheartedly on the storytelling.

<u>Story Mat and Characters:</u> After cutting out and assembling the story characters, children can use them on the Story Mat as the folktale is being told. The Story Mat is also a useful vehicle for encouraging groups of children to act out the folktale.

<u>Activities and Blackline Masters:</u> A set of hands-on activities are included to expand children's awareness of the culture. Developed with the idea of integrating all parts of the curriculum, the activities incorporate:

foreign language	math	science	dress
cooking	creative arts	drama	dance
music	creative writing	language arts	

Each activity is divided into the following sections for easy use:
- Cultural background
- Preparation
- Activity and Blackline Master

<u>Additional Literature:</u> A current bibliography of children's literature related to the culture is provided.

<u>Glossary:</u> The glossary includes foreign language words used throughout the unit. The pronunciation key is as follows:

a as in paper	ay	i as in bit	ih
a as in father	ah	o as in wrote	oh
e as in feed	ee	u as in flute	oo
e as in bed	eh	u as in mutt	uh
i as in fight	eye	u as in put	u

<u>Children and Families as Resources:</u> Whenever possible, encourage the children in your classroom who are familiar with the culture to share their knowledge and insights, and invite their families to enrich the program.

Table of Contents

Our Philosophy

The world is a smaller place these days, and children in our classrooms are from many cultures. This series offers stepping stones toward the goal of mutual respect among children of different backgrounds. The program offers an integrated curriculum, with whole class, cooperative group, and individual activities for the primary grades. Interviews were the primary source of information, giving the hands-on activities their authenticity, detail, and interest.

A special thank you to Bharati Kshirsagar and Meera Rao
for their invaluable contributions to this book.

The Old Woman in the Pumpkin

Retold by Betsy Franco

Indian Words in the Story:

sari (sah-REE)—woman's clothing made from a long piece of fabric wrapped around the waist and shoulders

chiura (CHYOO-rah)—a snack similar to trail mix

dal (dahl)—lentil beans commonly used in Indian cooking

curried fish (KUH-reed)—a fish stew; fish cooked in a spicy sauce made from locally grown spices

namaste (nah-MAHS-teh)—a greeting in the Hindi language

In eastern India lived a woman who was very old and very wise. One day she decided to visit her daughter who lived far away, on the other side of the forest.

First the old woman packed a gift for her daughter and some chiura to munch on during the journey. Then she carefully tied her sari and set off through the village. She walked steadily, not even stopping at the marketplace, until she came to the dark forest.

India

When the trees were thick and the sunlight was no longer visible overhead, she was surprised by a hungry jackal.

"It is time for lunch and I shall eat you, old woman," cried the jackal, licking his mouth.

The old woman thought quickly and replied,

"On the way to my daughter's house—
    I am bones,
    I am skin,
    I am small and thin.
On the way back from my daughter's house—
    I'll be plump
    I'll taste great,
    I'll be worth the wait."

 India

"Very well," sighed the jackal, "I will be waiting for you," and he slunk off into the forest.

The old woman nibbled her chiura. She made her way steadily through the dense trees until she was surprised by a hungry Bengal tiger.

"Ah hah, old woman," said the tiger, "just what I need for my lunch. Your journey is over."

 India

Again the old woman thought quickly and replied,

"On the way to my daughter's house—
    I am bones,
    I am skin,
    I am small and thin.
On the way back from my daughter's house—
    I'll be plump
    I'll taste great,
    I'll be worth the wait."

"I am very hungry, but I will wait for your return trip," growled the tiger in a low deep voice. "You will make a splendid meal."

 India

The old woman nibbled more of her chiura. When she had nearly reached her daughter's house, she was surprised by a large bear.

"I have had no luck catching my dinner today, but you, old woman, will do just fine," said the bear.

The old woman quickly replied,

> "On the way to my daughter's house—
> I am bones,
> I am skin,
> I am small and thin.
> On the way back from my daughter's house—
> I'll be plump
> I'll taste great,
> I'll be worth the wait."

"I guess you're right," said the bear. "I will be waiting right here when you return."

India

The old woman nibbled her chiura and continued on until she reached her daughter's house at the edge of the forest. At the doorway, her daughter knelt down, washed her mother's feet and waited with folded hands. The old woman touched her daughter's head in greeting and said, "Namaste."

When the old woman was safely in the house, she drank some water and presented her daughter with the gift she had brought—a beautiful red sari. Then she told of her dangerous journey through the forest.

"Your story frightens me," said the daughter. "What will you do?"

"Never mind that now, dear daughter. When the time comes, I will think of something," said the old woman, quieting her daughter's fears.

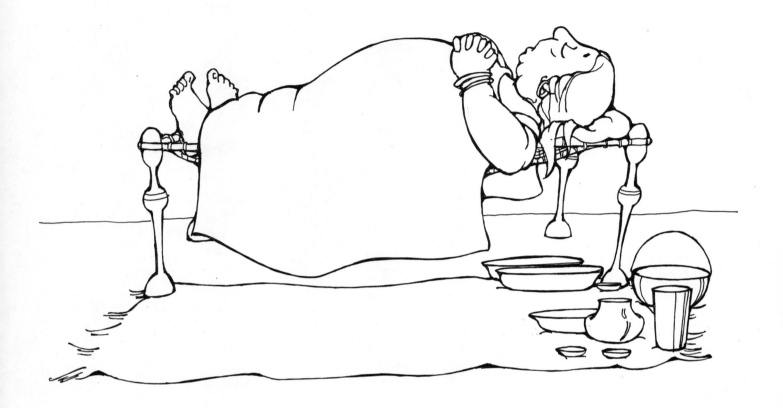

The kind daughter waited on her mother and cooked all the old woman's favorite foods— dal, vegetables, curried fish, and rice. The old woman slept soundly every night. After a week, she had truly become a bit plumper.

"It is time for me to return home, dear daughter," said the old woman one morning.

"But mother, you must not return through the forest. Please take the long way around, or you will surely be eaten on the way back," said the daughter.

But the old woman replied, "You need not worry about me. I may be old but my years have made me wise. All I ask is to use this large pumpkin from your garden, dear girl.

                                                                                       India

When they had hollowed out the pumpkin, the old woman squeezed inside and began rolling through the forest. She hadn't gone far before she came upon the bear, waiting for her on a tree stump. All the bear could see was a large pumpkin.

"Now that's odd," thought the bear. "What is a pumpkin doing in the forest?"

But he didn't think too hard, and he went back to waiting. On rolled the old woman in the pumpkin, until she came to the fierce Bengal tiger waiting on a thick tree limb.

India

"Now that's very odd," thought the tiger, "I don't think I've ever seen a pumpkin in the forest before."

But he didn't think too hard, and he went back to waiting. The old woman continued on until she was almost to the far edge of the forest. There was the nasty jackal, waiting for her on a soft bed of leaves.

"That's very very odd," thought the jackal. "A pumpkin is rolling through the forest!"

 India

Just then, the pumpkin hit a large boulder and "Craaaacck! POP!" the pumpkin split in two. The sound was so loud that the tiger and the bear came running through the forest to see what had happened.

"Why it was you after all, old woman," said the jackal. "You shall be my lunch today."

"No, she is my meal," said the tiger. "I have been waiting all week for her to return."

"Step aside! She is my lunch," snarled the bear.

The old woman thought quickly and replied, "It seems that the fiercest among you will have me for dinner."

 India

At that, the argument grew louder, and soon the three wild animals were clawing and biting and growling together in one tight ball.

As they rolled around on the forest floor, the old woman trotted out of the forest as fast as she could. She walked back through the village, not even stopping at the marketplace, and reached her home before the sun had set. That night, the woman who was very old and very wise slept soundly in her bed in eastern India.

India

Folktale Follow-Up

1. What do you notice about the way the characters are dressed?

The old woman and her daughter are dressed in cotton saris which consist of a piece of fabric six yards long wrapped around the body.

This story does not mention any men but you can share this information about men's dress with your students. Men would have two pieces of cloth wrapped around them. The bottom one, called a dhoti (DHOH-tee), serves as trousers, and the other cloth is draped around the shoulders and neck. Some men wear tunics on top.

Nowadays, this traditional clothing is worn by men mostly on special occasions, such as festivals. Older women always wear saris. Children normally wear modern dress—shorts, pants, skirts, and shirts.

2. Share facts about the houses.

No shoes are worn in the house. In fact, feet are washed before entering. (The daughter washed her mother's feet as a respectful greeting.) Inside the daughter's mud hut, there are mats on the floor with cushions, rather than chairs. Because of the hot climate, large mud pots are used to store water. Nowadays, some people live in homes similar to the mud hut in the story. In the city, homes are made of such materials as brick and cement, and are much more modern.

3. What can you say about Indian food from the story?

The old woman carried a snack of chiura, made of peanuts, raisins, coconut, and rice, For meals, mother and daughter ate fish curry, dal, vegetables and rice. The meals were served on a banana leaf that could be thrown to the cows—a perfect recycling system.

Other ways to use
The Old Woman in the Pumpkin

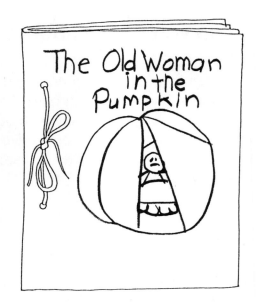

• Reproduce the story several times. Staple each copy inside a cover. Send the copies home with different children each night until all students have had an opportunity to share the story with their families. You may want parents to write a comment on the back cover explaining how their family shared the book and how they felt about it.

• If your students are at a level where they can read the story themselves, reproduce several copies for children to use for shared reading.

• Once your students are familiar with the story, reproduce the pictures on page 17. Have children cut the pictures apart and put them in the sequence they occur in the story. The pictures can then be used to...

1. Paste the story in order onto a large sheet of paper. (Have children refer to the original story if they have difficulty with the order.)

2. Create a picture book.
    • Paste the pictures into a book.
    • Use the pictures as you retell the story to a friend.

3. Rewrite the story.
    • Paste each picture to a sheet of writing paper.
    • Write about that part of the story.
    • Staple the finished pages together in order.
    • Make a cover for your book.

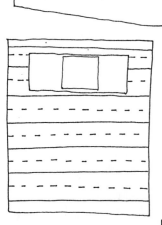

India

Pocket Chart Activity

Cut out the strips on pages 19-23 and place them in a pocket chart.

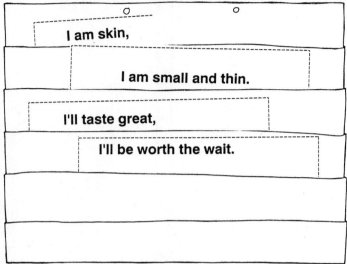

The chant can be read over and over again:

> • It can be read after the first reading of the folktale and chanted over and over again, following the name of the threatening animal. Then in the second reading of the folktale, the children can join in on the verses.

> • It can be read prior to the folktale.

Below are some suggestions for this particular chant:

> • Have the children point out any repetitious words:
> > *On the way* to *my daughter's house—*
> > > *I am* bones,
> > > *I am* skin,
> > > *I am* small and thin.
> >
> > *On the way* back from *my daughter's house—*
> > > *I'll be* plump,
> > > *I'll taste great,*
> > > *I'll be* worth the wait.

> • Ask the children to find the pairs of rhyming words:
> > skin—thin   great--wait

> • Encourage the children to make up unrhymed poems of their own using frames such as:

> > On the way to school (or to a birthday party)
> > I _____ , I _____ ,
> > I _____.
> > On the way home from school (or a birthday party)
> > I _____ , I _____ ,
> > I _____.

                                                           India

On the way

to my daughter's house --

from my daughter's house--

I am bones,

India

I am skin,

I'll be plump,

I'll taste great,

I'll be worth the wait.

India

I am small and thin.

On the way back

Story Mat

India

paste to page 25

Story Mat continued.

India

Characters

Use the characters on the Story Mat on pages 24-25 to act out the folktale **The Old Woman in the Pumpkin** as your teacher reads it, or act out the story in small groups.

Color in.
Cut out.
Fold.
Paste.

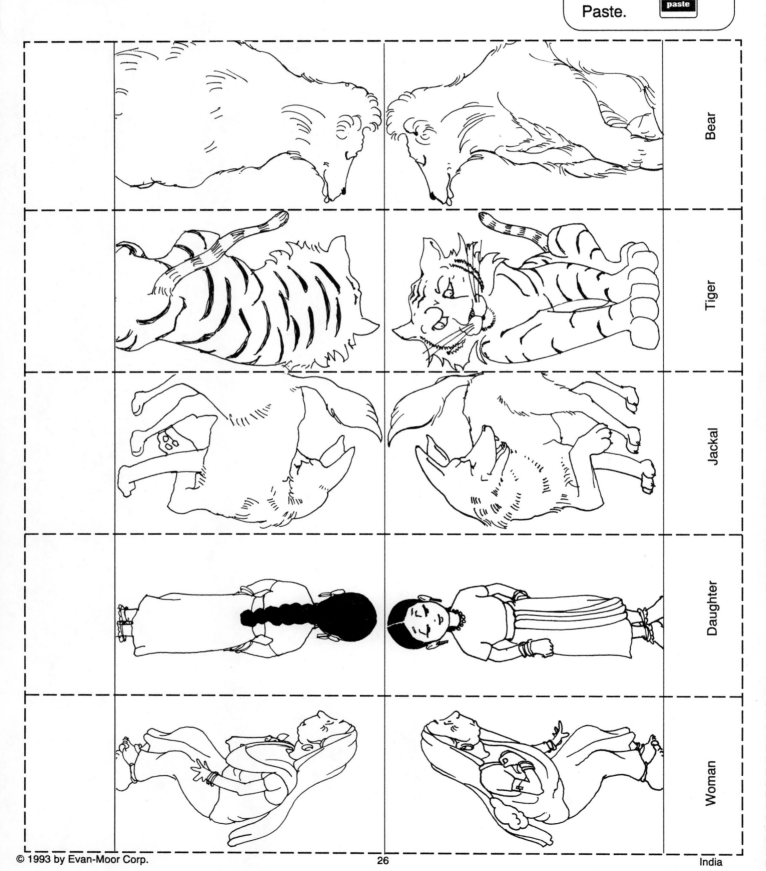

Bear

Tiger

Jackal

Daughter

Woman

India

Pumpkin

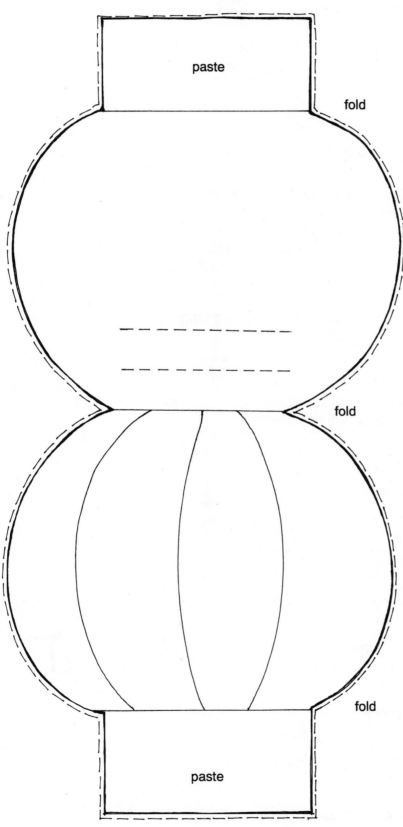

paste

fold

fold

paste

back   front

Learning Hindi

Cultural Background

India is made up of many states. Different languages are spoken in the different states, but the national language is Hindi (Hihn-dee). Some common phrases in Hindi are introduced in this activity.

Preparation

You might want to practice the pronunciation of each Hindi word below.

> **To write Hindi, each child will need:**
> • the form on page 29
> • felt pens

Activity

• Here are some Hindi words that you and your class can incorporate into your day:

Word	English	Pronunciation
Namaste	I greet you. (said with hands together and head bowed)	Nah-MAHS-teh
krupaya	please	kroo-pah-YAH
dhanyavad	thank you	DHAHN-yah-vahd
Chup!	Be quiet!	Choop
Kyon	Why?	kee-yoh(n)
Achha Phir Milengae	We'll meet again.	Ah-CHAH fihr mih-LEHN-gay
Mataji	mother	MAH-tah-jee
Pitaji	father	pih-TAH-jee

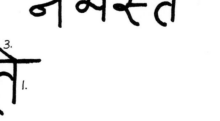

• Show the children how to write "Namaste" in Hindi The line across the top means it is one word. In fact, the words are written below the line.

Start here.

na   ma   s   te

• Give each child a copy of the form on page 29. Write "namaste" in Hindi in black. Then let them decorate the page with colored felt pens.

         India

Namaste

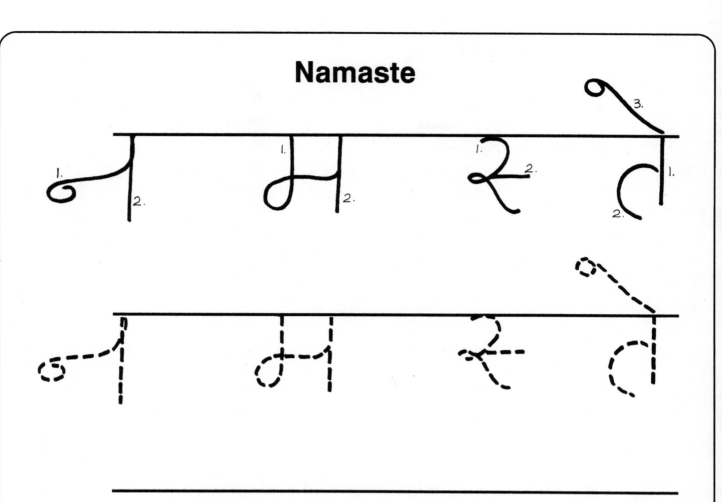

Playing Games with Sticks and Stones

Cultural background
The materials needed for playing children's games in India are often very easy to obtain. With a few sticks and a handful of stones, Indian children can have a lot of fun. They play games similar to "Jacks," "Hopscotch," "Marbles," and "Hide and Seek." They also play with bows and arrows and enjoy rolling a wheel using a stick. A sampling is given below.

Preparation

To play the stone game, each group of 2-3 children will need:
• 6 stones

Activity

Stone Game: Kallaata (Kah-LAAH-tah)

Kallu means stones; *aata* means games.

This game is similar to "Jacks" except that the ball is replaced by a stone. Therefore, the "ball" doesn't bounce. Instead it is thrown up and caught in the air after picking up a stone(s) on the ground. In the first round, the five stones are picked up one at a time, then two at a time (2/2/1), three at a time (3/2), and so forth. The second round involves pushing the stones into a "cave" formed by the left hand, one at a time, two at a time, and so forth.

Preparation

To play the wheel game, each group of children will need:
• a bicycle wheel or Hula Hoop
• a long dowel or stick

Activity

Wheel Game

The child sets a bicycle wheel rolling and coaxes it along with a stick, while running alongside.

Preparation

To play Paandi, each group of 2-3 children will need:
• chalk
• stones

Activity

Hopscotch: Paandi (Paahn-DEE)

Paandi is played the same way as hopscotch. The "court" can be drawn in two different ways.

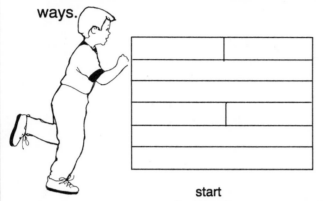

or

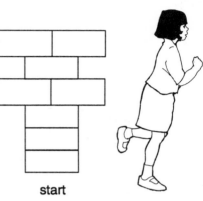

In the first round, each player throws a stone on the first space (then the second space, third space, and so on) and hops back and forth, avoiding the space with the stone. In the second round, each player throws the stone to claim a "home." Initials are written in the home space in mud (or chalk). Then the game is played as in the first round, except that player 1 can't step on player 2's home, and vice versa. Note that each time a player has completed a full round successfully, he/she claims an additional home space. Pretty soon there are very few squares open.

Preparation

To play the stick game, each pair of children will need:
• a long dowel about 1 foot long
• a short dowel about 6-8 inches long

Activity

Stick Game: Gulli-Danda (Goo-LEE Dahn-DAH)

The object of this game is to hit the shorter stick (the "gulli") as far as possible using the longer stick. The player sets the gulli on an uneven surface (such as an uneven sidewalk) and hits one end of it with the longer stick so the gulli "jumps up." When the gulli is in the air, the player bats it as far as he/she can. The player who bats the gulli the farthest is the winner.

Discuss safe ways to play this game so no one is accidentally hit by a stick.

Playing a Board Game

Cultural Background

The game Pagade (Puh-gah-DE), is a very popular game in India among children of all ages. It is similar to the American game "Sorry." A simplified version of Pagade is described below.

Preparation

> **To play the game, groups of four will need:**
> • a copy of the form on page 33
> • two dice, each marked 1, 3, 4, 6
> (You can put "correction tape" over the 2 and 5 on normal dice.)
> • 4 pawns of the same color for each player. Chips, or interlinking cubes can be used.

Activity

• Set up your players this way to start:

• The object of the game is to send all of your players around the entire board counterclockwise and into the "Home" space.
• On your turn, roll the dice. Find the sum and move one pawn that number of spaces. Or move one pawn the number of spaces on the first die and another pawn the number on the second die.
• If you land on a space occupied by an opponent's pawn, your opponent's pawn is sent back to the start.

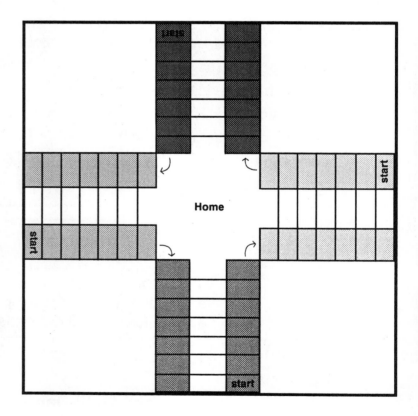

Additional Rules for Older Children
• If two of your pawns are on the same space, they are called a "pair." A pair can send a single pawn back to the start, but only a pair can send another pair back to the start. Pairs can move together if you roll a double. Pairs can split up at any time.
• If one of your pawns is ready to enter the white path toward "Home" it must wait until at least one of your pawns has sent an opponent's pawn back to start.

         India

A Version of Pagade

(Puh-gah-DE)

start

start

Home

start

start

India

Drawing Flour Designs

Cultural Background

According to Hindi custom, rice powder (or rice paste) is used to create geometric designs on the floors and entrance ways of houses. This art form is called "Rangoli" (RUHN-goh-lee) or "Alpana" (ahl-pah-NAH). Designs are generally made of white rice paste, but sometimes red is used. Flowers and colored powders are used to decorate the inside of the design. There are two ways to create the patterns. Some are done freehand. Others are done according to a geometric pattern of dots.

Preparation

To make a design with flour, each group will need:
• black paper
• paper cups filled with flour
• pencils

To make designs with chalk, each group will need:
• a copy of the form on page 35 duplicated on colored paper
• white and colored chalk

Activity

Let your groups circulate between two activities:

1. Flour designs: Have children outline large geometric shapes by letting the flour fall through their fingers onto black paper. Some children may want to draw a shape first in pencil. (Note: These designs cannot be saved.)

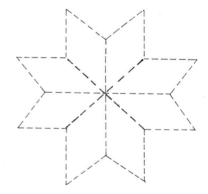

2. Chalk designs: Have the children complete the design shown on page 35 using white chalk. Colored chalk can be used to decorate the outsides and insides of each shape. Spray the completed designs with fixative. Encourage the children to find any geometric shapes and to count the number of times each shape appears.

Some children may want to create their own designs using templates of pattern block shapes. Save the designs to display while celebrating Divali (see page 39).

     India

An Indian Design

Copy this design.

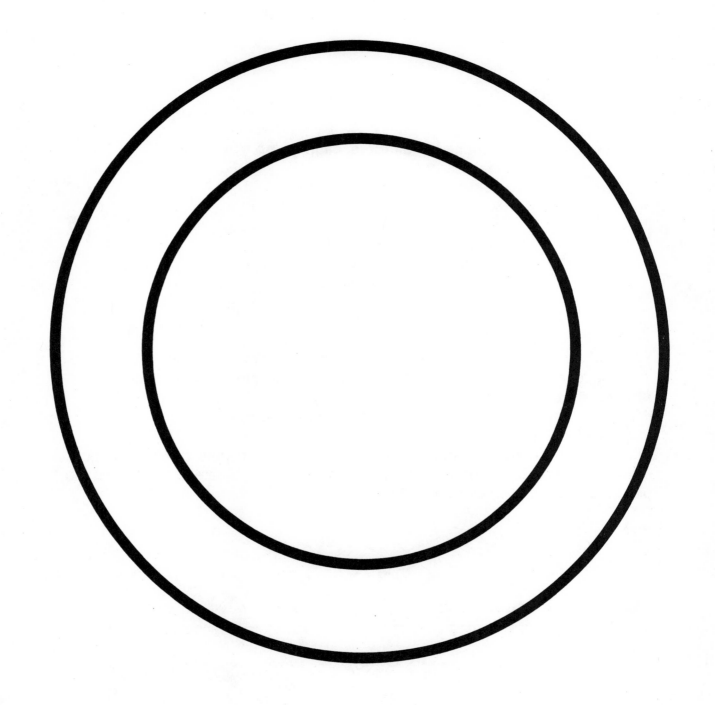

Creating Indian Paintings

Cultural Background

Indian paintings often depict a story from ancient books of tales and traditions, such as the Ramayana (Rah-MAH-yah-nah). Indian artists use bright colors, such as gold, red and green, and they include intricate details and patterns. A decorative border often sets off the painting. Sometimes paintings are done in miniature, such as on the backs of playing cards.

Preparation

To make the pictures, each group needs:
- crayons or felt pens
- gold colored crayons or pens
- white paper
- a colored paper border to glue on the paper
- glue

You might want to find a few library books with samples of Indian paintings.

Activity

• As a whole class, have the children discuss important events in their lives—the birth of a sibling, getting a family pet, celebrating a holiday, learning a skill or sport.
• Have each child choose one event to draw.
• Show the children some samples of Indian art such as those on page 37. Point out the detail and the borders.
• Let each child draw his/her scene in bright felt pens or crayons, using lots of gold.
• When the picture is complete, help the children write (or dictate) a story about the picture or a description explaining the picture.

Samples of Indian Art

India

Making Instruments

Cultural Background

The distinctive sound of Indian music is partially due to the types of instruments played. There are many types of drums; some are played with the hand, others with sticks. Flutes are always made of bamboo, not metal. (The longer the flute, the lower the sound.) Clarinets are played, as well as tambourines and sitars. A sitar is a stringed instrument. The jaltarang (JAHL-tah-rung) is an unusual instrument consisting of thirteen thin glasses filled with different amounts of water. They are struck with two wooden sticks.

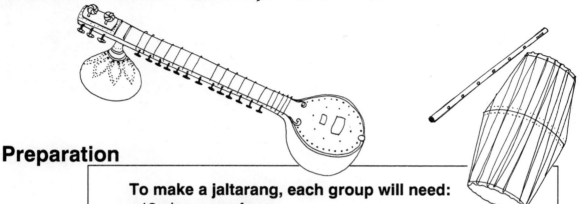

Preparation

To make a jaltarang, each group will need:
• 13 glasses or fewer
• chopsticks or knitting needles
• water
You will need to collect some instruments, such as:
• flutes
• tambourines
• bells
• aluminum cans for drums
You will need to find a cassette of Indian music.
(often available from the public library)

Activity

• Divide the children into groups.
• Let each group create a jaltarang.
• Encourage the groups to let each child be responsible for pouring the water into one glass and testing its sound.
• Let the children take turns playing the instrument using chopsticks or knitting needles.
• Pass out the other instruments.
• Play some traditional Indian music, and have the children play along.

     India

Celebrating Divali

Cultural Background

Divali (Dih-vah-LEE) is an autumn festival signifying the triumph of good over evil. It is celebrated throughout India for two days in October or November, at the time of a new moon. Thus, the night is nearly pitch black. People buy new clothes and decorate their homes with flowers and flour designs. Small oil lamps made from baked mud are filled with oil, lit, and placed on every windowsill and roof. At night, there are fireworks displays. Large figures of Ravana (RAH-vah-nah), a ten-headed creature signifying greed and evil, are filled with firecrackers and set off.

Preparation

To make "oil lamps," each child will need: • clay • a piece of red cellophane for the flame • glue	**To make "sparklers," you will need:** • dowels or sticks • strips of colored cellophane tape
To make Ravana, each group of ten will need: • 10 3" tag paper circles • felt pens • a ruler or yard stick • tape	**You will need:** • the floor designs made on page 35 • drums and tambourines for the sound effects of firecrackers • stapler • glow in the dark pens or paints to decorate Ravana and sparklers (optional)

Activity

• Have the children create the lamps, Ravana, and the sparklers:

Red cellophane glued in clay.	Each child can make one face on a circle. They can be stapled together and taped to a stick.	strips of colored cellophane

dowel

• Decorate the room with the flour designs, and put the clay lamps all around, on the windowsills.
• Turn off the lights and draw the shades. Parade around with the sparklers and the 10-headed creatures. Sound effects can be created with drums and tambourines.

Exploring Indian Clothing

Cultural Background

Cotton is grown in India, and it is a very practical fabric because of the hot climate. For special occasions, the girls and women wear saris (sah-REES). These are pieces of cotton or silk fabric, about 6 yards (540 cm) long, wrapped around the body and worn over blouses and skirts. The boys and men wear a tunic and loose pants made of cotton. Traditionally, men may also wear two pieces of cotton fabric. One piece, the dhoti, is wrapped around the waist and legs and another is thrown over the shoulders and neck. On normal days, girls wear cotton pants or skirts and the boys wear shorts and shirts.

Preparation

> **To make the graph, you will need:**
> • a large graph on which to record children's results
>
> **To tie the sari and dhoti, you will need:**
> • directions on page 41
> • sheet or table runner for the sari
> • two halves of a sheet for the men's wear

Activity

• Discuss different types of fabric.
• Have the children predict from which material most of their clothing is made.
• Have the children check the tags indicating type of material on their own clothing (shirts, dresses, sweatshirts, coats).
• Start a graph of the types of fabrics they find. Compare the results to their predictions.

cotton	polyester	nylon	wool

• Demonstrate tying a sari and dhoti, and let the children practice. See page 41 for instructions.

India

Note: a full size flat sheet, cut in half long ways, can be used

Tying a sari:

waist end | 3 yards (275 cm) | shoulder end

1. Put the waist end in front of you and sweep the shoulder end around behind you. Tuck the corner of the waist end into your skirt or pants.
* A real sari would be wrapped around twice.

2. Place the shoulder end under your right arm, around the front, and over your left shoulder.

3. There should be left over material between the two ends. Pleat it with your fingers like an accordion fold. Tuck it into the front of your waist band.

pleats

4. Let the shoulder end drape down off your shoulder.

Tying a dhoti and a fabric for the shoulders:

3 yards (275 cm) | 3 yards (275 cm)

1. Tuck one end of the fabric into your pants on the left side. Bring the fabric around the back.

2. Bring the fabric to the front and pleat it with your fingers. Tuck it into your front waist band.

3. Drape the other piece of fabric around your shoulders and neck.

India

Making a Snack

Cultural Background

Chiura (CHYOO-rah) is an Indian snack that is eaten like trail mix. To make the Indian version, you saute garlic powder, onion flakes, red pepper, and red chilis in a tablespoon of oil to add flavor. Slivers of dried coconut and flat rice and small strips of rolled out garbanzo dough are also sauted. Then peanuts, cashews, and raisins are added. For the American version, Rice Krispies are substituted for flat rice, and Chinese chow mein noodles replace the garbanzo flour.

Preparation

Each group will need:

- a duplicate of the directions on page 43
- measuring spoons, measuring cup, mixing bowl
- 3/4 C (180 ml) Rice Krispies or Chex Cereal
- 1/2 C (120 ml) roasted peanuts and cashews
- 1/2 C (120 ml) raisins

- 1/4 C(60 ml) coconut slivers
- 1/4 C (60 ml) Chinese chowmein noodles
- pinch of salt
- pinch of sugar
- pinch of red chili pepper

Activity

- Organize the children into small groups and distribute the ingredients and copies of the instructions on page 43.

India

Chiura (chyóo-ra)

1. Add 3/4 C (120 ml) Rice Krispies

2. Add 1/2 C (120 ml) peanuts & cashews

3. Add 1/2 C (120 ml) raisins

4. Add 1/4 C (60 ml) coconut slivers & 1/4 c (60 ml) Chinese noodles

5. Add pinch of salt

6. Add pinch of sugar

7. Add pinch of red chili pepper

8. Mix. Eat. Enjoy.

India

How to Use the Counting Chart

Use the Counting Chart on page 45 to acquaint children with how to count to ten in Hindi. Leave the chart up in the classroom for the students to refer to while you are doing this unit on India.

Counting Chart

1 ek	2 do
ayk	dthoh
3 teen	4 char
dtheen	chahr
5 panch	6 chae
pahnch	cheh
7 sat	8 aath
sah	aath
9 now	10 dus
now	dthuhs

1. Provide students with many opportunities to count in Hindi.

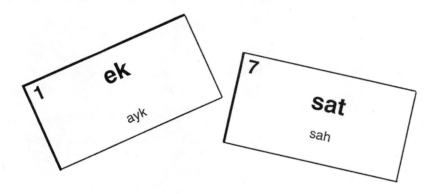

1 ek ayk

7 sat sah

10 dus dthuhs

2. Students may enjoy creating a counting book with Hindi symbols and words. Each page of the book could be a different number and the pictures could be of typically Indian things.

3. Make a copy of the Counting Chart. Cut the numbers apart and let the students sequence the numerals as they count.

India

Counting Chart

1 **ek** ayk	**2** **do** dthoh
3 **teen** dtheen	**4** **char** chahr
5 **panch** pahnch	**6** **chae** cheh
7 **sat** sah	**8** **aath** aath
9 **now** now	**10** **dus** dthuhs

 India

The Flag of India

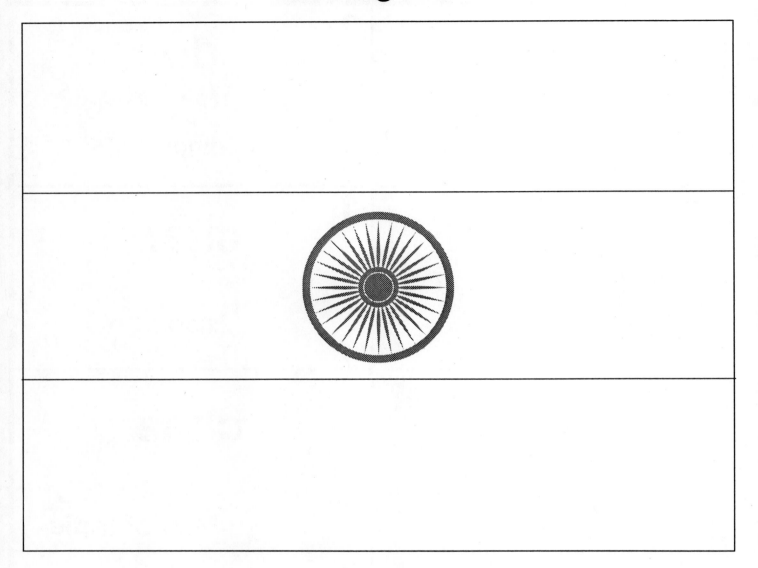

This is the flag of India.
It is orange at the top, white in the middle and green on the bottom.

There is a blue wheel in the center of the white band.

India is about one third the size of the United States of America,
but it has more than three times as many people.

India is a country of
 • many people
 • many religions
 • many languages
 • many cultures

India

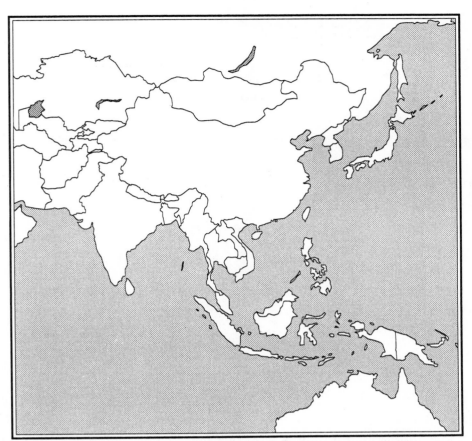

Map of Asia

Find India on this map of Asia.
Color it orange

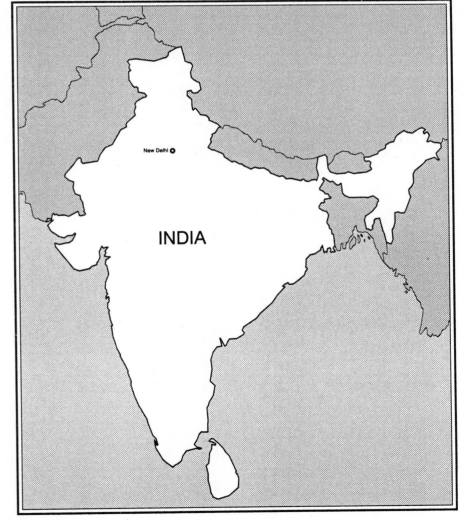

New Delhi

INDIA

Map of India

47

India

Glossary

Pagade (Puh-gah-DEH) — a board game played with pawns and dice

alpana (ahl-pah-NAH) — floor design created with rice powder or paste

chiura (CHYOO-rah) — a snack similar to trail mix

curry (KUH-ree) — any of a number of Indian dishes that include a curry powder made from a mixture of locally-grown spices

dal (dahl) — lentil beans, commonly used in Indian dishes

dhoti (DHOH-tee) — a cotton cloth worn by men; wrapped around the waist and legs

Divali (Dih-vah-LEE) — Indian festival celebrating the triumph of good over evil

gulli-danda (Goo-LEE-dahn-DAH) — a game played with two sticks

Hindi (Hihn-DEE) — national language of India

jaltarang (JAHL-tah-rung) — a musical instrument consisting of thirteen glasses filled with different amounts of water; played by striking glasses with two wooden sticks

kallaata (Kah-LAAH-tah) — a stone game similar to "Jacks"

namaste (nah-MAHS-teh) — a greeting in Hindi

paandi (paahn-DEE) — a game like hopscotch

Ramayama (Rah-MAH-yah-nah) — a sanskrit epic poem telling ancient tales and traditions

rangoli (RUHN-goh-lee) — floor designs created with rice powder or paste

Ravana (RAH-vah-nah) — a ten-headed demon signifying evil and greed; included in the Divali festival

sari (sah-REE) — traditional woman's clothing; a piece of fabric wrapped around the waist and shoulders, worn over a blouse and skirt

Additional Resources

The Blue Jackal by Marcia Brown; Charles Scribner's Sons, 1977

The Monkey and the Crocodile: A Jataka Tale by Paul Galdone; Clarion Books, 1969

Favorite Fairy Tales Told in India by Virginia Haviland; Little, Brown and Company, 1973

The Golden Deer by Margaret Hodges; Charles Scribner's Sons, 1992

It All Began With a Drip, Drip, Drip... by Joan M. Lexau; The McCall Publishing Company, 1970

Take a Trip to India by Keith Lye; Franklin Watts, Inc., 1982

Seasons of Splendour: Tales, Myths, and Legends of India by Madhur, Jaffrey; Atheneum Children's Books, 1985

The Stonecutter: An Indian Folktale by Patricia Montgomery Newton; Putnam Publishing Group, 1990

Once a Mouse by Marcia Brown; Charles Scribner's Sons, 1961

Foolish Rabbit's Big Mistake by Martin Rafe; Putnam Publishing Group, 1985

The Beautiful Blue Jay and Other Tales of India by John W. Spellman; Little, Brown and Company, 1967

The Magic Cooking Pot by Faith M. Towle; Houghton Mifflin Company, 1975

The Great Minu by Beth P. Wilson; Follett Publishing Company, 1974

Seven Blind Mice by Ed Young; Philomel, 1992